The British Museum

FIND TOM IN TIME

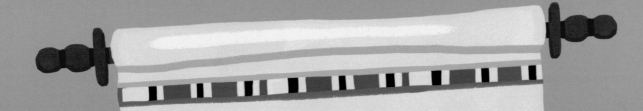

Ancient Egypt

About Ancient Egypt

Ancient Egypt was founded in the lands around the River Nile, in the same place that modern-day Egypt lies today. The first settlers started building cities over 6,000 years ago, and 900 years later the first king or **PHARAOH** united the country. Ancient Egyptian life and culture flourished under many different rulers over thousands of years, with amazing temples and pyramids being built that still stand today. Some of the places that Tom visits in this book may not have existed together at the same time, but they were all part of ancient Egyptian culture and history.

Get ready to meet . . .

Tom

Granny Bea

Digby the cat

and spot the hidden scarab beetle in every scene!

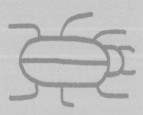

First published 2019 by Nosy Crow Ltd
The Crow's Nest, 14 Baden Place,
Crosby Row, London SE1 1YW
www.nosycrow.com

This edition published in 2021

978 1 78800 101 4 (HB)
978 1 78800 705 4 (PB)

Nosy Crow and associated logos are trademarks
and/or registered trademarks of Nosy Crow Ltd.

Published in collaboration with the British Museum.

Text © Nosy Crow 2019
Illustrations © Fatti Burke 2019

The right of Nosy Crow to be identified as the author and Fatti Burke
to be identified as the illustrator of this work has been asserted.

A CIP catalogue record for this book is available from the British Library.

Printed in China.
Papers used by Nosy Crow are made from wood
grown in sustainable forests.

1 3 5 7 9 8 6 4 2 (HB)
1 3 5 7 9 8 6 4 2 (PB)

Contents

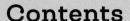

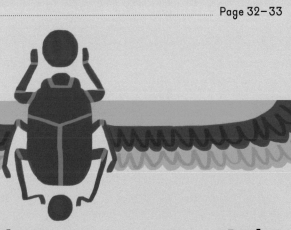

INTRODUCTION

Tom was an ordinary boy, most of the time.
He was clever and brave and he loved adventure.

Tom's grandmother, Bea, was an ordinary grandmother, most of the time. She was clever and brave, and a little bit mischievous, and she loved adventure, too. Which was just as well, since her job was digging in the dust and the dirt to discover how people used to live. Granny Bea was an **ARCHAEOLOGIST**.

Granny Bea's cat, Digby, did not like digging in the dust and the dirt. Or getting wet. Or missing his meals. In fact, Digby did not like adventure at all. Digby's favourite thing was to find a nice soft bed and have a nap.

One ordinary afternoon, Granny Bea called Tom up to her study.

"Here," said Granny Bea, giving Tom a heavy cloth bag to hold. "I thought you might want to look at this," she added, holding up something small and blue in the shape of an eye.

"What is it?" asked Tom, forgetting about the bag for a moment.

Granny Bea smiled. "It's an **AMULET**. Ancient Egyptians carried them to protect themselves from harm, and this protective eye symbol was thought to keep children safe."

Tom stretched out his hand to touch the amulet and . . . **WHOOSH!**

THE PYRAMIDS

Tom was in ancient Egypt! He couldn't believe it. Had Granny Bea known this would happen? He was in a desert, surrounded by towering pyramids.

Suddenly, Digby jumped out of the bag Tom was holding and ran off. Oh no! He must have been sleeping in there. Where had that naughty cat gone?

CAN YOU SPOT?

- A sphinx
- A child pretending to be a mummy
- Tom
- A worker who has tripped and dropped his water
- Someone eating some bread
- Digby the cat
- A high priest wearing a leopard skin

The pyramids were built out of heavy blocks of stone, which were brought over from nearby **QUARRIES** on boats and hauled up ramps on wooden **TOBOGGANS**. This is why the pyramids were built close to the River Nile.

The pyramids were designed to protect a **PHARAOH**'s body and his belongings after he died. When a pharaoh came to power, he started planning his pyramid straight away, because they could take up to 25,000 men 20 years to build!

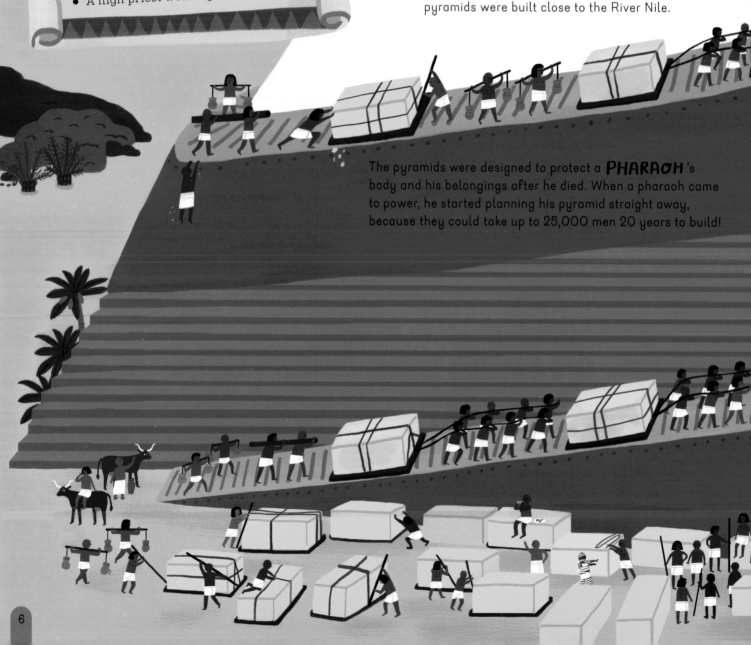

A large statue called the **SPHINX** stood in front of the pyramids. It had the body of a lion and the head of a pharaoh.

7

A FUNERAL PROCESSION

A funeral procession went past and a priest squinted at Tom. Uh oh! Tom needed a disguise. He found some strange clothes in the bag Granny Bea had given him.

"That's weird," he thought, as he put them on. "It's almost as if Granny Bea knew I would need these."

Suddenly, he thought he spotted Digby.

Ancient Egyptians believed that when someone died, they would go on a journey to the **AFTERLIFE**. A person could only get into the afterlife if they passed a series of tests, so a funeral was held 70 days after they died to help get them ready.

CAN YOU SPOT?

- Digby the cat
- Two flute players
- A priest in a jackal mask
- Tom
- Someone holding one blue jar
- A falcon
- A woman holding papyrus scrolls

At a funeral procession, family and friends would walk behind the coffin with dirt on their heads, beating their hands against their arms and bodies to show how upset they were. Servants walked behind them, carrying the things that would be buried with the dead person, and priests led the way at the front.

Women sang sad songs, and pretended to be the goddesses **ISIS** and **NEPHTHYS**, who were the chief **MOURNERS** in ancient Egyptian religion, while other people played instruments.

BURYING a mummy

Tom followed the funeral party towards a pyramid. A priest in a jackal mask stood a gleaming golden coffin up and started chanting. It was amazing, but a bit scary too.

Just then, a cat raced out of the pyramid and through the crowd of mourners. Could it be Digby?

CAN YOU SPOT?

- A scribe painting on a roll of papyrus
- Tom
- A mummified cat
- Digby the cat
- A pair of royal golden sandals
- A guest taking a sneaky nap
- A basket of eggs

Ancient Egyptians believed that they needed their human body in order to reach the afterlife, so pharaohs, wealthy people and even some animals were turned into mummies.

After being entombed, ancient Egyptians believed the dead person would be carried by boat to an underworld called **DUAT** that was full of terrible dangers and difficult tests. Only if they managed to pass every test would the dead person finally be allowed to enter a **PARADISE** called the **KINGDOM OF THE DEAD**.

The mummy was put inside one or more beautiful coffins. Outside, under the rays of the sun, a priest would perform a special ceremony called the "**OPENING OF THE MOUTH**" to wake up the mummy's senses, such as sight, smell and taste. The coffin was then taken inside the pyramid or tomb and put inside a stone **SARCOPHAGUS**.

The RIVER NILE

Tom raced through the crowd after Digby. He soon found himself next to an enormous river. There were boats everywhere and people carrying baskets and crates.

Tom found paw prints leading to the river, but he couldn't see Digby. Perhaps that naughty cat was napping somewhere?

The River Nile was very important for ancient Egyptians. They used it to travel around Egypt and to trade goods with other countries, particularly with the ancient Greeks.

Fishermen went out on small boats made of reeds, while larger ships carried soldiers and **MERCHANTS** and were used by rich noblemen for relaxing day trips.

Ships coming into ancient Egypt brought cedar wood and **EBONY**, precious metals and stones, leopard skins, spices and exotic animals like baboons. In return, the Egyptians sold grains, **PAPYRUS**, perfume, **ALUM** and **NATRON** (which were used for dying fabric).

CAN YOU SPOT?

- Digby the cat
- Two protective eye symbols
- An angry-looking hippo
- Tom
- A fisherman who has fallen in
- A sleeping baboon
- A nobleman and his dog having a day out on the river

Hippos and crocodiles caused a lot of trouble for boats because they could easily tip them over. Hunting hippos with spears was a popular (and dangerous) sport!

FARMLAND

Suddenly, a fisherman fell into the water with a huge splash. With an angry yowl, a soaking-wet Digby leaped out of one of the boats and raced away.

As Tom followed, he saw farmers working on the land. It was very muddy. Where was Digby now?

Farmers were very important in ancient Egypt because they produced all the food, from crops to cows. But they had to work very hard. Every year, the Nile flooded and this brought lots of **NUTRIENTS** to the land, which helped the crops to grow. But when the Nile flooded, the farmers didn't get any time off. They had to join the thousands of workers building the pyramids instead.

CAN YOU SPOT?

- Children collecting leftover grain
- Two monkeys picking dates
- Digby the cat
- Tom
- A naughty donkey
- Farmers crushing grapes with their feet
- A water-damaged house

Farmers dug canals of water from the Nile to the fields and towns further away. They used a **SHADUF**, which was a long wooden pole with a bucket hanging from one end, to collect and transport water.

Instead of machines or tractors, farmers used **OXEN** to pull ploughs and break up the soil, donkeys to carry grain, and monkeys to pick dates from the trees.

THE MARKETPLACE

Tom followed Digby across the fields and finally reached a town. He found himself in a bustling market. There were a lot of people shouting at each other and buying and selling all kinds of things.

Tom spotted a cat through the crowds. And another . . . and another.

Which one was Digby?

Ancient Egyptians had no money. Instead they traded goods that had the same value. They could also pay with small pieces of gold and silver measured in **DEBEN** (a traditional ancient Egyptian measure of weight).

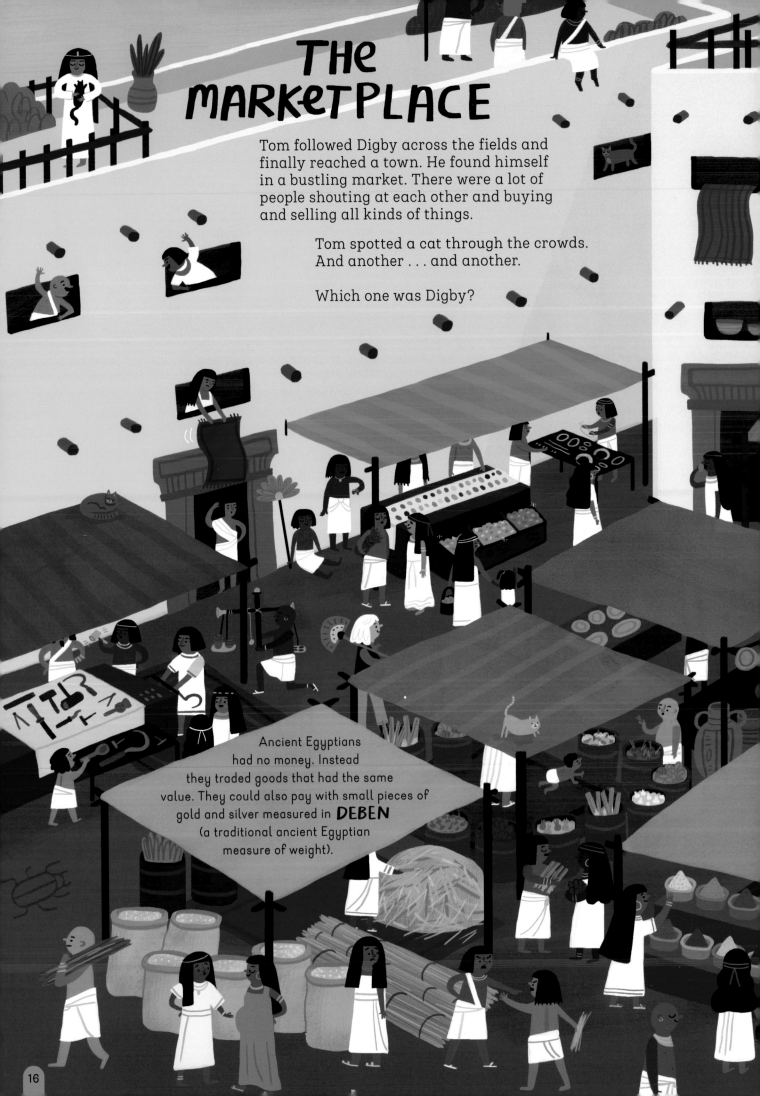

A sack of wheat equalled around one deben, while a cow equalled around 50 deben. Some ancient Egyptians carried a pair of **WEIGHING SCALES** in order buy and sell their goods.

CAN YOU SPOT?
- Two men having an argument
- Tom
- Someone carrying a very heavy sack of grain
- A cat that has stolen a fish
- Digby the cat
- A woman buying amulets
- A stall selling tools

The market was where ancient Egyptians bought and sold their food, tools and furniture, and where they exchanged gossip, too!

The Temple

Tom ran after Digby and soon found himself outside a grand temple.

The walls were painted with funny symbols and pictures, and the entrance was lined with fierce-looking statues.

But where had Digby gone? Tom hoped it wasn't inside . . .

CAN YOU SPOT?

- Digby the cat
- A statue that is missing a paw
- A priestess carrying a statue
- Tom
- Acrobats entertaining the crowds
- A statue of a god who looks like a cat
- A bird stealing an offering of fruit

Temples were very **SACRED**, secret places, where the ancient Egyptians believed their gods and goddesses lived. Only the pharaoh, priests and priestesses were allowed inside. Everyone else prayed outside.

The temple was guarded by rows of special sphinxes with the head of a ram. Inside, the ceilings were painted with stars to look like the sky and the walls were decorated with scenes of the pharaohs making offerings to the gods.

Ancient Egyptians believed there were over one hundred different gods and goddesses. **RA** was god of the sun, **ISIS** was the chief goddess and had magical powers, and **OSIRIS** was the god of the dead.

On special occasions, priests carried the statues of the gods outside for everyone to see and worship them.

SCRIBE SCHOOL

Tom saw a flash of orange. Digby! He raced around the corner of the temple and found a group of boys writing strange symbols on blocks of stone.

Tom scratched a picture of a cat in the sand. One of the boys laughed at Tom's drawing and pointed to a cat racing away from the centre of town. Digby!

Not many children in ancient Egypt went to school. Those that did were very lucky. They started aged five and studied for up to 10 years. After this, they could become **SCRIBES**.

Scribes were very well respected in ancient Egypt because they could read and write **HIEROGLYPHS**, a way of writing the Egyptian language using small pictorial signs. A scribe had many jobs. They had to write receipts for market sales, note down medical texts, record the pharaoh's glorious deeds and even write down magic spells to be put in tombs.

CAN YOU SPOT?

- A priest wearing a leopard skin writing on the wall
- A boy who is covered in ink
- A scribe who has broken his reed brush
- A boy drawing some graffiti on a wall
- A scribe taking a nap
- Digby the cat
- Tom

Girls couldn't become scribes. Some may have learned to read and write, but only for fun. Instead, they learned how to spin cloth, weave baskets, or bake bread.

The EMBALMING WORKSHOP

Tom gave the boy a thumbs-up and raced after Digby towards a building. It seemed to be some kind of workshop. Inside was a busy room filled with people, priests and . . . dead bodies!

Tom looked around nervously. Surely Digby wouldn't want to stay here for long!

Making a mummy was a long process. First, the brain was pulled out with a hook pushed through the nose. Next, a small cut was made on the left-hand side of the body and the internal organs were taken out.

The liver, lungs, intestines and stomach were cleaned and stored in **CANOPIC JARS**. The heart was left inside the body because the ancient Egyptians believed the heart was the centre of a person's personality and intelligence.

CAN YOU SPOT?

- Digby the cat
- Tom
- A priest wearing a leopard skin taking a nap
- A collection of amulets
- A smelly string of garlic
- A broken canopic jar
- A scribe carrying too many scrolls

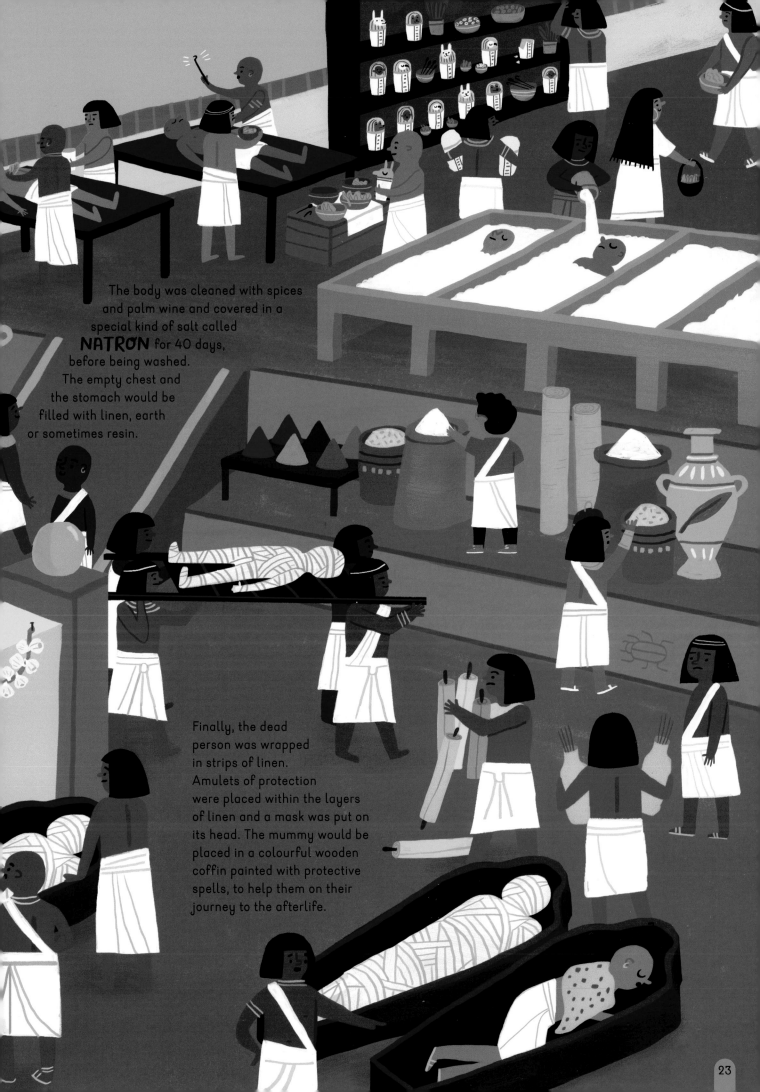

The body was cleaned with spices and palm wine and covered in a special kind of salt called **NATRON** for 40 days, before being washed. The empty chest and the stomach would be filled with linen, earth or sometimes resin.

Finally, the dead person was wrapped in strips of linen. Amulets of protection were placed within the layers of linen and a mask was put on its head. The mummy would be placed in a colourful wooden coffin painted with protective spells, to help them on their journey to the afterlife.

HOUSING

Tom tripped over a long orange tail. It was Digby! The surprised cat bolted out of the door of the workshop and raced back towards town. Tom ran after him. "Digby!" he shouted.

But his cat had vanished. Tom stopped by a row of houses. Inside he could hear voices and laughter.

A typical house had three or four rooms: a living room, a storeroom (with a cellar below), a bedroom and a kitchen courtyard, with steps up to the roof.

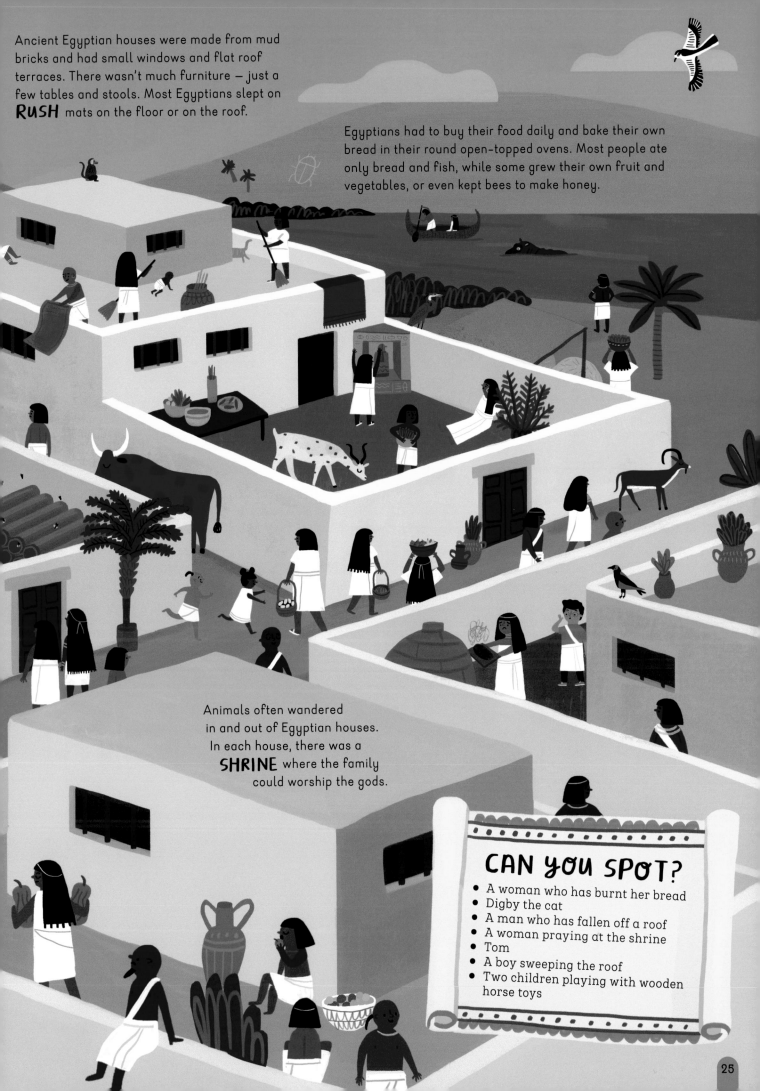

Ancient Egyptian houses were made from mud bricks and had small windows and flat roof terraces. There wasn't much furniture — just a few tables and stools. Most Egyptians slept on **RUSH** mats on the floor or on the roof.

Egyptians had to buy their food daily and bake their own bread in their round open-topped ovens. Most people ate only bread and fish, while some grew their own fruit and vegetables, or even kept bees to make honey.

Animals often wandered in and out of Egyptian houses. In each house, there was a **SHRINE** where the family could worship the gods.

CAN YOU SPOT?
- A woman who has burnt her bread
- Digby the cat
- A man who has fallen off a roof
- A woman praying at the shrine
- Tom
- A boy sweeping the roof
- Two children playing with wooden horse toys

A NOBLEMAN'S HOME

Tom spotted Digby leaping out of a window and scampering away down the road. He followed until the cat jumped over the gate of a huge, grand-looking house.

Carefully, Tom crept in behind him. He hoped they wouldn't get into trouble!

A rich ancient Egyptian's home might have had a hall, a kitchen, a grain store and cellar, several bedrooms, a shrine, and a bathroom.

They would also have had stables and beautiful walled gardens, sometimes with freshwater pools where pet fish were kept. Servants would have had to change the water regularly to keep it fresh.

The furniture in grand houses was made from expensive wood, as well as **IVORY** and gold. The windows were high to keep the heat out, and the walls were covered in plaster and painted with beautiful pictures.

Servants and **SLAVES** looked after the house and the family. They lived at the back of the house, and did all of the cooking, cleaning and gardening.

CAN YOU SPOT?

- A child playing with a wooden rattle
- A servant carrying a fish
- Tom
- A servant fanning a noblewoman
- An angry goose chasing a child
- Digby the cat
- Someone who has fallen into the pool

BANQUET

Suddenly, Tom found himself in the middle of a huge feast. There were a lot of people talking and laughing, and the food smelled absolutely delicious!

Digby loved to eat, so he must be nearby.

Rich Egyptians often held great **BANQUETS** for all their friends. They were served by slaves and servants, while musicians and acrobats put on performances for the guests.

Women wore cones of sweet-smelling wax on their heads. As the night went on, the wax melted, cooling their heads and making their hair look nice and shiny.

CAN YOU SPOT?

- A mouse stealing some food
- A servant carrying too many dishes
- Digby the cat
- A woman whose wax cone has fallen off
- Tom
- A guest who has spilled their drink
- Some people cooling down on the roof

At a feast, the host and hostess would sit on a raised platform, while the guests sat on stools. There were no knives and forks, so everyone ate with their fingers.

At these feasts, guests would eat meat dishes like ox, **GAZELLE**, duck and goose, with lots of fresh fruit and vegetables, followed by sweet cakes and pastries. All the food was cooked on the roof to avoid fires.

FeSTIVAL ON THE RIVeR

Tom heard a meow. It was Digby running away with a piece of duck!

He followed the naughty cat to the river. A huge festival was taking place, but it was difficult to see over the crowd.

Finally, Tom spotted Digby in the arms of . . . Granny Bea!

Festivals took place throughout the year to celebrate the gods. During a festival, statues of gods were taken out of the temples and carried by priests in special gold-painted boats to other temples.

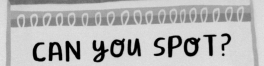

CAN YOU SPOT?

- A child with their pet dog
- Someone carrying bread
- Digby the cat and Granny Bea
- Three priests wearing leopard skins burning incense
- A man with a bird on his head
- Tom
- Three ceremonial cows

Ancient Egyptians believed that if they kept their gods happy, they would be protected from harm. People also visited the **TOMBS** of their relatives during festivals. They brought their dead relatives offerings and had big feasts at the tombs.

The most important priests and priestesses led the way, carrying palm leaves and **INCENSE** burners, followed by cows that were to be the **SACRIFICE** for the gods, and musicians and dancers.

HOme

Tom ran up to Granny Bea and gave her a huge hug.

As he did, there was a sudden . . . **WHOOSH!**

. . . and just like that, Tom was home!

"Did you have fun, Tom?" asked Granny Bea, as Digby jumped down from her arms and raced straight for his comfy basket. She carefully placed the eye-shaped amulet in a glass case on her desk.

"You were with me all along!" said Tom.

"Well, you didn't think I'd let you have all that fun on your own, did you?" replied Granny Bea with a wink. . . and Digby just purred.

EGYPT

Can you go back and spot Granny Bea in every scene?

SOLUTIONS

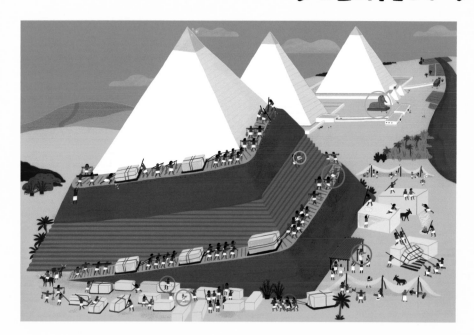

THE PYRAMIDS
Pages 6–7

- A sphinx
- A child pretending to be a mummy
- Tom
- A worker who has tripped and dropped his water
- Someone eating some bread
- Digby the cat
- A high priest wearing a leopard skin

A FUNERAL PROCESSION
Pages 8–9

- Digby the cat
- Two flute players
- A priest in a jackal mask
- Tom
- Someone holding one blue jar
- A falcon
- A woman holding papyrus scrolls

BURYING A MUMMY
Pages 10–11

- A scribe painting on a roll of papyrus
- Tom
- A mummified cat
- Digby the cat
- A pair of royal golden sandals
- A guest taking a sneaky nap
- A basket of eggs

The RIVER NILE
Pages 12–13

- Digby the cat
- Two protective eye symbols
- An angry-looking hippo
- Tom
- A fisherman who has fallen in
- A sleeping baboon
- A nobleman and his dog having a day out on the river

FARMLAND
Pages 14–15

- Children collecting leftover grain
- Two monkeys picking dates
- Digby the cat
- Tom
- A naughty donkey
- Farmers crushing grapes with their feet
- A water-damaged house

THE MARKETPLACE
Pages 16–17

- Two men having an argument
- Tom
- Someone carrying a very heavy sack of grain
- A cat that has stolen a fish
- Digby the cat
- A woman buying amulets
- A stall selling tools

SOLUTIONS (continued)

The Temple
Pages 18–19

- Digby the cat
- A statue that is missing a paw
- A priestess carrying a statue
- Tom
- Acrobats entertaining the crowds
- A statue of a god who looks like a cat
- A bird stealing an offering of fruit

SCRIBE SCHOOL
Pages 20–21

- A priest wearing a leopard skin writing on the wall
- A boy who is covered in ink
- A scribe who has broken his reed brush
- A boy drawing some graffiti on a wall
- A scribe taking a nap
- Digby the cat
- Tom

The EMBALMING WORKSHOP
Pages 22–23

- Digby the cat taking a nap
- Tom
- A priest wearing a leopard skin taking a nap
- A collection of amulets
- A smelly string of garlic
- A broken canopic jar
- A scribe carrying too many scrolls

HOUSING
Pages 24–25

- A woman who has burnt her bread
- Digby the cat
- A man who has fallen off a roof
- A woman praying at the shrine
- Tom
- A boy sweeping the roof
- Two children playing with wooden horse toys

A NOBLEMAN'S HOME
Pages 26–27

- A child playing with a wooden rattle
- A servant carrying a fish
- Tom
- A servant fanning a noblewoman
- An angry goose chasing a child
- Digby the cat
- Someone who has fallen into the pool

BANQUET
Pages 28–29

- A mouse stealing some food
- A servant carrying too many dishes
- Digby the cat
- A woman whose wax cone has fallen off
- Tom
- A guest who has spilled their drink
- Some people cooling down on the roof

SOLUTIONS (continued)

FESTIVAL ON THE RIVER
Pages 30–31

- A child with their pet dog
- Someone carrying bread
- Digby the cat and Granny Bea
- Three priests wearing leopard skins burning incense
- A man with a bird on his head
- Tom
- Three ceremonial cows

Glossary

AFTERLIFE Beginning a new life after death

ALUM Chemical used for dying cloth and making leather

AMULET Small piece of jewellery or object thought to give protection against danger or evil

ARCHAEOLOGIST Someone who studies history by digging up and examining historical objects

BANQUET Large celebratory feast shared by many people

CANOPIC JARS Four special jars used to store a mummified person's liver, lungs, intestines and stomach that were buried alongside the mummy

DEBEN Traditional ancient Egyptian measure of weight, used to work out how much silver or gold to pay for something

DUAT The **UNDERWORLD**

EBONY Dark and slow-growing wood from a tree grown in Egypt and other warm places

EMBALM To use salt or other chemicals to stop a body from rotting

GAZELLE Small, fast, deer-like animal

HIEROGLYPHS A way of writing using pictures and symbols to make up words and sounds

INCENSE A material that is burned to produce a pleasant smell

ISIS Ancient Egyptian goddess of magic and wife of **OSIRIS**

IVORY Material made from the teeth or tusks of animals such as hippopotamuses and elephants

KINGDOM OF THE DEAD Ancient Egyptian name for **PARADISE**

MERCHANT   Person who buys and sells things for a living

MOURNER   Someone who attends the funeral of a friend or relative

NATRON   Type of salt used to dry dead bodies as part of the **EMBALMING** or mummification process

NEPHTHYS   Ancient Egyptian protective goddess of the dead

NUTRIENTS   Substance that provides food to help plants to grow

OPENING OF THE MOUTH CEREMONY   A ceremony performed outside a pyramid or tomb to wake up a mummy's senses and prepare them for their journey into **DUAT**

OSIRIS   Ancient Egyptian god of the **UNDERWORLD**

OXEN   Large, slow, cow-like mammal

PAPYRUS   Paper-like material made from reed stems

PARADISE   The final place the ancient Egyptians believed a person travelled to after death, where they lived with the gods in a perfect version of their life on Earth

PHARAOH   King or ruler

QUARRY   Place where stone is cut from

RA   Ancient Egyptian god of the sun

RUSH   Waterside plant with long thin leaves used for weaving mats and baskets

SACRED   Special or holy

SACRIFICE   To kill an animal as an offering to a god or gods

SARCOPHAGUS   Stone coffin

SCRIBE   Person who could read and write **HIEROGLYPHS**

SHADUF   Long wooden pole with a bucket hanging from one end to collect and transport water

SHRINE   Place of worship

SLAVE   Person who is the property of someone else and must obey their owner

SPELL   Magical charm or chant

SPHINX   Mythical creature with a human head and a lion's body

TOBOGGAN   A long, narrow vehicle on flat runners, similar to a sledge, used by the ancient Egyptians to slide heavy blocks of stone over sand

TOMB   Place for burying a dead person, either underground or in a special building

UNDERWORLD   The first place ancient Egyptians believed a person travelled to after death, where they had to pass a series of tests in order to enter **PARADISE**

WEIGHING SCALES   A piece of equipment used for weighing things

Index

40